MATHS CHALLENGES
FOR ABLE PUPILS

Written by
WENDY SINGLETON

First Published
April 05 in Great Britain by

PUBLISHING

A CIP record for this work is available from the British Library

ISBN-10: 1-904904-28-9
ISBN-13: 978-1-904904-28-1

Typeset by Educational Printing Services Limited

Educational Printing Services Limited
Albion Mill, Water Street, Great Harwood, Blackburn BB6 7QR
Telephone: (01254) 882080   Fax: (01254) 882010
E-mail: enquiries@eprint.co.uk   Website: www.eprint.co.uk

One of the particular difficulties facing teachers in Primary schools today is that of challenging able pupils in mixed ability, and sometimes mixed age, classes. In many mixed ability classes this can be achieved by well-planned and effective differentiation. In the main, the whole class can work together through the Framework with their varying needs being met by differentiating such things as task, outcome, expectation, resource or support. There are, however, some situations which differentiation alone will not resolve, for example:

- Pupils in the class whose ability is so far in advance of their peers that much of the time they do not need the teaching and consolidation which has been planned for the class as a whole.

- Times when the teacher needs to focus on assessment tasks which are inappropriate for the more able.

- Pupils who need to have the opportunity to work independently, perhaps on extended tasks.

- Pupils whose ability level means that they sometimes finish work quickly, but the teacher is necessarily occupied with others.

The difficulties presented by having very able pupils in mixed ability classes become more acute as they become older. It is almost always inappropriate to allow these pupils to work from the Key Stage 3 programme of study, so some other means has to be found to stretch and challenge them. Probably the best way to do this is to give them tasks which:

- Demand a broader and deeper understanding of the mathematics relevant to their age group.

- Allow them to take responsibility for their own work.

- Require them to apply their mathematical knowledge in unfamiliar situations.

- Involve higher order thinking skills.

- Are of a more extended nature, requiring perseverance and determination.

- Present them with the opportunity to pose their own questions of the 'What if ....?' kind to extend their investigations.

This book provides a bank of activities for able pupils in upper Key Stage Two, which will meet the criteria outlined above and at the same time provide the teacher with some help towards overcoming the difficulties presented by mixed ability classes.

Some tasks and activities are of a longer, more extended nature, sometimes involving research, which may require pupils to use the Internet. There is scope in many activities for pupils to explore a line of enquiry which they determine themselves. This should be encouraged.

Solutions are generally given on the teacher page and headed 'Solutions' or 'Solutions and notes', but in the sections headed 'Challenges for pupils' it is sometimes more appropriate for answers/acceptable responses to be given in italics after the question.

In the main, it is intended that able pupils will be given a copy of the pupil page and expected to work on these activities independently of the teacher. Adult intervention should be kept to a minimum. As far as possible it should be confined to introducing and explaining to the pupil(s) the more difficult 'Challenges for pupils'. These pages are not intended to be given to the pupil(s) – they should be viewed as teacher guidance for appropriate extension work.

1. Building blocks

Start with the numbers 1, 2, 3, 4 and 5 in the bottom row of building blocks and sum them to the top as shown. The number in each block is the sum of the two numbers below it.

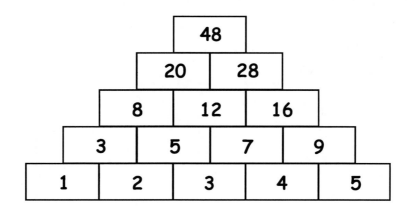

Try this again with the same numbers in the bottom row but in a different order. Do you get the same number or a different one in the top block?

Change the order of the numbers in the bottom row again and repeat. Investigate how many different numbers you can get in the top block. (Remember, you may only use the numbers 1, 2, 3, 4 and 5 in the bottom row.)

1. Building blocks

Challenges for pupils

- What is the largest total you can get in the top block?
- What is the smallest?
- How must you arrange the numbers in the bottom row to make sure you get the largest and smallest totals at the top?
- How can you make sure the total in the top block is an odd number?
- How can you make sure it is even?
- Try out your theories by starting with 5 different numbers in the bottom row, but keep them small.
- Now use an arrangement of blocks like this one and use the numbers 1, 2 and 3 in the bottom row.

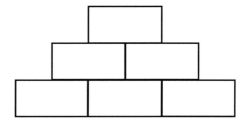

- Investigate all the different possible totals in the top block. (*3, 1, 2 and 2, 1, 3 will both give the total of 7 at the top, 1, 2, 3, and 3, 2, 1 will both give a total of 8 and 1, 3, 2 and 2, 3, 1 will both give 9.*)
- Instead of 1, 2, 3 use the letters a, b and c in the bottom row. What do you get in the top block?
  Solution:

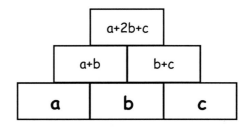

- Use this to help you to predict what the three possible totals in the top block could be if you started with 2, 5 and 7 in the bottom row and then check your answer. *(16, 19 and 21)*

- Use what you have learnt to help make generalisations and predictions about totals of building blocks with 4 numbers at the bottom, and then with 5. (You will need to use letters in the bottom row first instead of numbers.)

Solution:

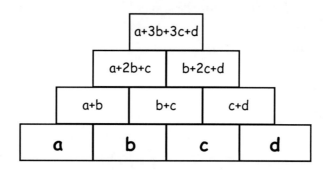

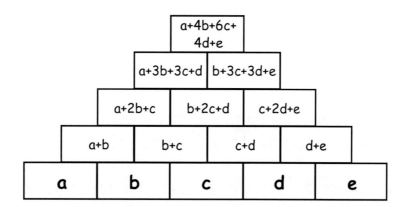

- Can you see any connections between the numbers in Pascal's Triangle on page 18 and the work you have just been doing? *(Example: Look at the numbers in the generalisation for results with 4 numbers in the bottom row:*
  a + 3b + 3c + d
  The numbers 1, 3, 3, 1 appear in the 4th row of the triangle.)

- Can you use Pascal's Triangle to help you work out what all the largest and smallest possible totals would be starting with 1, 2, 3, 4, 5 and 6 in the bottom row?

1. Building blocks

Solutions

The order of the numbers in the bottom row affects the total in the top block. There are 120 different possible arrangements of the 5 numbers but not all 120 give different totals. For example:

All these arrangements will give a total of 61 (the maximum possible):

1, 4, 5, 3, 2
1, 3, 5, 4, 2
2, 4, 5, 3, 1
2, 3, 5, 4, 1

All these arrangements will give a total of 35 (the minimum possible):

5, 2, 1, 3, 4
5, 3, 1, 2, 4
4, 2, 1, 3, 5
4, 3, 1, 2, 5

The outer 2 numbers and the centre number in the bottom row play the most significant part in affecting the total in the top block:

• The larger the number in the centre, the larger the total will be.

• The largest possible number in the middle, combined with the 2 smallest numbers on the outer edges produces the largest total.

• The reverse of this will give the smallest possible total.

1. Building blocks

2. Snakes alive!

Snakes follow very strict rules of movement. They move a certain number of squares in a straight line, then turn clockwise through 90° before moving again in a straight line.

This snake is a 1, 2, 3 snake and moves like this:

It moves along one square in a straight line then turns, moves two squares in a straight line and turns again. It moves three squares and turns, then goes back to moving one square before turning again, and so on.

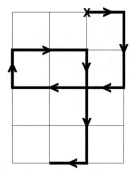

Continue with this snake.

Investigate other snakes.

2. Snakes alive!

Challenges for pupils

- Make the following snakes:
    - 1, 2, 3
    - 2, 3, 4
    - 3, 4, 5 and so on
    - Can you predict what a 19, 20, 21 snake would look like?

- Make these snakes:
    - 1, 2, 4
    - 1, 2, 5
    - 1, 2, 6 and so on
    - Can you predict what a 1, 2, 20 snake would look like?

- Try some other snake 'families', for example:
  2, 4, 6;   4, 6, 8;   6, 8, 10 etc.

- Will a 3, 2, 1 snake make the same track as a 1, 2, 3 snake? Try some other 'backwards' snakes.

- What about '4 step snakes', such as 1, 1, 2, 4, or '5 step snakes'?

- Make up your own investigations with snakes and see if you can find connections and make predictions.

2. Snakes alive!

Solutions

This 1, 2, 3 snake will arrive back at its starting point.

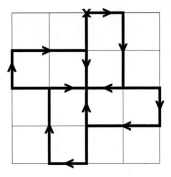

A 2, 3, 4 snake will also arrive back at its starting point but its track will look different.

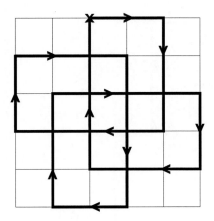

2. Snakes alive!

Solutions (continued)

A 1, 2, 4 snake will arrive back at its starting point but leave a different track from the other two.

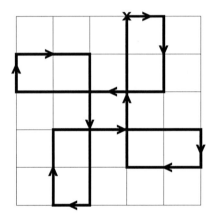

A four step snake such as 1, 1, 2, 4 will spiral.

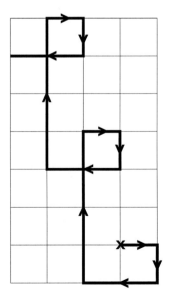

3. Braille

A man called Louis Braille invented a system of printing letters and numbers that can be 'read' by blind people. (When you have finished this investigation you might like to find out more about Louis Braille and his alphabet for the blind.)

This system known as Braille, is made up of different numbers of raised dots arranged within an invisible 2 x 3 grid. Each different arrangement represents a different symbol (letter or number).

Some symbols are represented by just one dot within the grid, some by two dots, some by three and so on.

A 'one dot' symbol could be, for example:

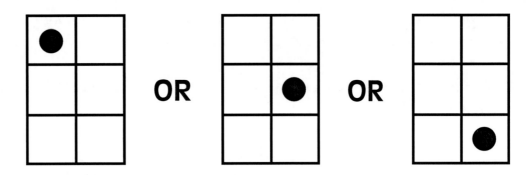

A 'two dot' symbol could be, for example:

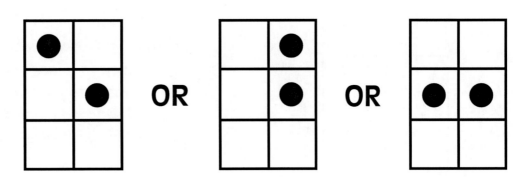

Investigate how many different symbols can be represented in this way, using from 1 to 6 dots.

3. Braille

Challenges for pupils

- How many different ways can you arrange from 1 to 4 dots in a 2 x 2 grid? *(16)*
- What about up to 8 dots in a 2 x 4 grid? Estimate how many possible arrangements you think there would be. *(Not for the faint hearted! There are 256 ways!)*
- Can you see any connections between the numbers in Pascal's triangle on page 18 and the work you have just been doing? *(Example: On the 2 x 2 grid of dots there is 1 way to 'place' zero dots, 4 ways to place one dot, 6 ways to place two, 4 ways to place three and 1 way to place four, giving the number sequence 1, 4, 6, 4, 1. This sequence of numbers can be found on the 5th row of Pascal's triangle. The numbers for the 2 x 3 grid are 1, 6, 15, 20, 15, 6, 1 - the 7th row of the triangle.)*
- If you have tried the 2 x 4 grid problem, how can you check your results by using Pascal's triangle?
- How close was your estimate of the number of possible arrangements of up to 8 dots?
- How many ways are there of arranging up to 12 dots in a 2 x 6 grid?
- So far you have only looked at grids with an even number of squares (2 x 2, 2 x 3, 2 x 4, etc) What else could you try? *(Grids with an odd number of squares as in the example below.)*

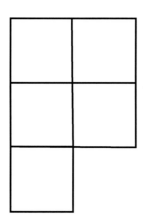

On this grid there are:
1 way to 'place' zero dots
5 ways to place one dot
10 ways to place two dots
10 ways to place three dots
5 ways to place four dots
1 way to place all five

3. Braille

Solutions

There are:

6 ways to place one dot
15 ways to place two dots
20 ways to place three dots
15 ways to place four dots (the two empty positions in the grid occur in the same locations as the two dots)
6 ways to place five dots (the empty positions occurring in the same locations as the one dot)
1 way to place six dots (which corresponds to the one way to 'place' zero dots)
A total of 64 ways

Using Pascal's Triangle

The solution to the number of possible arrangements on any grid can be found in the row whose <u>second</u> number is the same as the number of spaces in the grid, ie:

<u>5</u> spaces in grid ⟶ row starting 1, 5 (6th row)

<u>8</u> spaces in grid ⟶ row starting 1, 8 (9th row)

The pattern of numbers in the row gives the number of possible arrangements for the necessary number of spots (see solution to '5' grid on previous page).

The total for each row gives the total number of arrangements for that grid.

4. Pascal's triangle

Pascal's triangle is so called because it is often said that a mathematician called Blaise Pascal devised it in the 17th century. However, there is evidence that it is much older than this and was known to the Chinese people in the 13th and 14th centuries. (Perhaps you would like to try to find out more about Pascal and the Chinese triangle when you have completed this investigation.)

You need several copies of Pascal's Triangle on page 18.

Look at the numbers in the triangle. Each number is found by adding together the two numbers immediately above it. For example the 20 in row seven is the sum of the two tens in the row above. (The only exceptions to this rule are the 1s which begin and end every row, because they do not have two numbers above them.)

There are many patterns to be found if you know where to look.

You will find the counting numbers in a straight line in the triangle, but not on a horizontal row!

Look at another straight line parallel to this one, a line that begins with the numbers 1, 3, 6, ... What can you say about the numbers in this line? How do they grow? What are they called?

Look at other lines of numbers parallel to these two. Can you spot any more patterns? Can you explain how the numbers in each line grow?

You should be able to find each line of numbers you spot in two different places within the triangle.

Write down anything else you find out about Pascal's Triangle.

4. Pascal's triangle

Challenges for pupils

- Look at each horizontal row in the triangle and total its numbers. For example, the row 1, 3, 3, 1 has a total of 8 and the row 1, 2, 1 has a total of 4. Do this for all the horizontal rows (use a calculator when the numbers get bigger) and keep a record of the totals. Can you see a pattern to the totals? (You might be able to predict the totals without adding the numbers as you move down the rows.)

- Starting with a clean copy of Pascal's Triangle, colour in all the multiples of 2. On another clean copy, colour in all the multiples of 3. Starting with a clean copy each time colour in all the multiples of each number up to 9. When you have finished them all compare the results. What have they all got in common?
  (Tip: Use the tests for divisibility and the visual patterns you begin to see to help you. You won't need to do calculations on **every** number to know whether to colour it in or not!)

4. Pascal's triangle

Solutions and notes

See Pascal's Triangle below with patterns indicated as follows:

Key

■   Counting numbers

□   Triangular numbers (these 'grow' by adding on one more each time, i.e. 1 (+2), 3 (+3), 6 (+4), 10 (+5),15 (+6) ...etc.

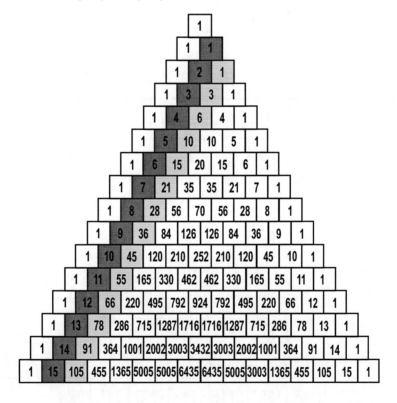

Multiples of each number form triangular patterns within Pascal's Triangle, some being more clearly visible than others depending on how many horizontal rows are displayed overall - the more rows in the triangle, the clearer the patterns become. Therefore it may be useful to have extended versions of Pascal's Triangle available with, say, an additional ten rows. Many children will enjoy working out the growing numbers (using a calculator of course!)

4. Pascal's triangle

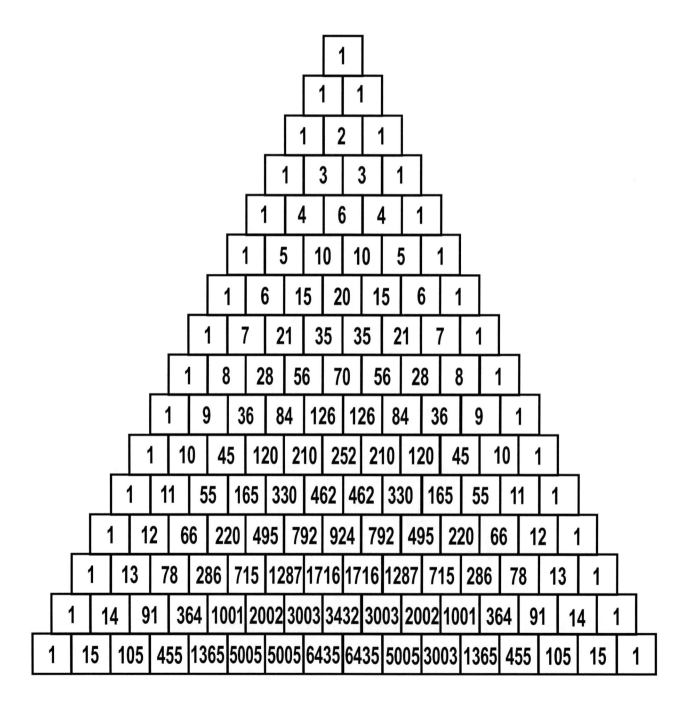

5. Paving stones

Square lawns are made up of square pieces of turf, for example:

This is a 2 x 2 lawn

This is a 5 x 5 lawn

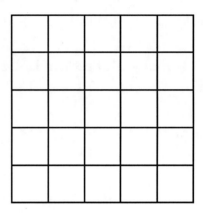

A lawn is surrounded by paving stones the same size as a piece of turf so a 3 x 3 lawn, for example, would need 16 paving stones to surround it:

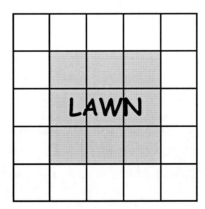

Investigate the relationship between the size of a lawn and the number of paving stones needed to surround it. (Keep your lawns quite small, no more than 8 x 8.)

Record your results systematically in a table.
Explain what you find out.

5. Paving stones

Challenges for pupils

- Use your table of results to work out how many paving stones would be needed to surround a lawn measuring 12 x 12.

- How many stones would be needed to surround a lawn measuring 50 x 50? Or 100 x 100?

- Generalise your findings by showing how you would work out how many paving stones (N) would be needed to surround a lawn measuring L x L.

- Investigate lawns having different lengths but always measuring one unit wide, for example:

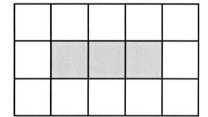   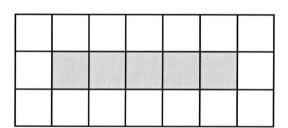

How would you calculate the number of paving stones needed for lawns of this shape? (*The general rule is N = 2L + 6 or, alternatively, the general rule for any rectangular lawn is below.*)

- Investigate other rectangular lawns in the same way so that you would be able to work out the number of stones needed to surround any lawn measuring L x B. (*The general rule for rectangular lawns is N = 2 (L + B) + 4, which would also be correct for lawns of unit width as above.*)

5. Paving stones

Solutions

Pupils should be encouraged to display their findings as a table:

Side length of lawn (L)	No. of paving stones (N)
1	8
2	12
3	16
4	20
5	24
etc.	etc.

By doing this they will more readily see the relationship which is:

$$N = 4L + 4$$

and can be explained in this way:

To completely surround it, a lawn needs one paving stone for each unit of its perimeter (in the case of a square lawn that is equal to four times its side length). Plus four more stones for the corners. For example:

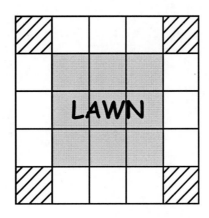

6. Up the garden path

Here's another stony problem!

A garden path **always** measures two units in width. However it can be **any number** of units in length, but must always be made up of stone slabs measuring two by one units. The shortest path that can be made uses one stone slab like this:

A path could be made up of, say, 4 slabs like this:

Or the same four slabs could be arranged in different ways:

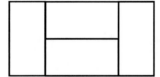 

Can you make paths that are made using 3 slabs? How many different possible arrangements of the three slabs can you find?

Investigate paths using 1, 2, 3, 4, 5, 6 and 7 slabs.

Record your results systematically in a table.

Explain what you find out.

6. Up the garden path

Challenges for pupils

•   Look at your table of results. From this can you work out how many different arrangements there would be for 8 slabs, 9 slabs etc.?

•   Explain how these numbers are growing.

•   Extend the table of results so that you can find out the answer to these questions:

>   •   How many possible arrangements would there be with 12 slabs?

>   •   What is the smallest number of slabs you would need to be able to show over 1000 different arrangements?

•   **Estimate** (then work out)

>   •   The smallest number of slabs you would need to be able to show over 4000 different arrangements.

>   •   How many different arrangements are possible with 20 slabs?

6. Up the garden path

Solutions

Pupils should be encouraged to display their findings as a table:

Number of slabs in path	1	2	3	4	5	6	7
Number of arrangements	1	2	3	5	8	13	21

The number of arrangements forms a sequence known as the Fibonacci sequence, where each new term is found by adding together the two previous ones.

The sequence can be continued in this way until all the numbers required to answer the questions are displayed:

Number of slabs in path	1	2	3	4	5	6	7	8	9	10
Number of arrangements	1	2	3	5	8	13	21	34	55	89

Number of slabs in path	11	12	13	14	15	16	17	18	19	20
Number of arrangements	144	233	377	610	987	1597	2584	4181	6765	10946

7. Fun with Fibonacci

If you have done the investigation called 'Up the garden path' (pages 23 & 24) you will recognise this number sequence:

1, 1, 2, 3, 5, 8, 13, 21, 34, 55, 89, ...

It is called the Fibonacci sequence, named after the 13th century mathematician who first devised and studied it.

Can you see how the numbers grow? Work out the next 5 numbers in the sequence.

This number sequence has some very interesting properties. Try these investigations:

- Choose any three adjacent numbers in the sequence, for example, 5, 8, 13. Square the centre number (8 x 8 = 64) and multiply the other two together (5 x 13 = 65).
Make a note of these two numbers (64 and 65).
Now choose another three adjacent numbers (perhaps 8, 13 and 21, or 34, 55 and 89) and repeat.
Each time you do this with three adjacent numbers, make a note of the answers to the calculations.
Do this a few times with different sets of three numbers and explain what you find.

- Choose any pair of adjacent numbers, for example 21 and 34.
Divide the smaller number by the larger one using a calculator and write down the answer that appears in the display (21 ÷ 34 = 0.617647).
Repeat this with other pairs of adjacent numbers, carefully writing down the answer each time (55 ÷ 89 would give the answer 0.6179775).
When you have done this with at least 7 or 8 pairs, explain what you have noticed about the answers.

- Start at the beginning of the sequence and find the difference between each number and the one that comes after it (find the difference between 1 and 1, then 1 and 2, 2 and 3, 3 and 5, 5 and 8 etc.). Write these differences down as you go. Can you explain what is happening and why?

7. Fun with Fibonacci

Challenges for pupils

- Choose any five adjacent numbers. Square the middle number and write down the answer. Multiply the outer two together and write down the answer. Finally, multiply the remaining two together and write down the answer. What do you notice? *(The answers are consecutive numbers.)* Will this work with any set of five adjacent numbers? *(Yes, except with numbers very early in the sequence.)*

- Look for similar patterns in sets of four adjacent numbers and six adjacent numbers. *(With four adjacent numbers the inner two and the outer two must be multiplied together to give two consecutive numbers. These patterns break down with six plus adjacent numbers.)*

- Find a chart or a table that converts miles to kilometres. Find the number of kilometres equivalent to 5 miles, 13 miles, 55 miles etc. What do you notice? How do you think you might be able to use this property of the Fibonacci sequence? *(5 miles is approximately 8km, 13 miles is approximately 21km and 55 miles is roughly equal to 89km and so on. Any pair of adjacent numbers will give roughly the miles/km equivalents and so is useful as a quick converter when travelling abroad.)*

- Find out what you can about the Golden Section, the Golden Ratio and the Golden Rectangle. All are related to the Fibonacci sequence and are to be found in art, architecture and nature.

7. Fun with Fibonacci

Solutions and notes

The Fibonacci sequence up to the 20th term is:

1, 1, 2, 3, 5, 8, 13, 21, 34, 55, 89, 144, 233, 377, 610, 987, 1597, 2584, 4181, 6765, 10946

The numbers grow by adding together the last two terms to find the next one (55 + 89 = 144 etc.). The first two numbers of the sequence are both 1 because the sequence actually starts at 0:
0, 1, 1, 2, 3 .... The rule now holds throughout.

Number trios will always generate two consecutive numbers:
     21, 34, 55 will give 1156 (34^2) and 1155 (21 x 55)
     89, 144 and 233 will give 20736 (144^2) and 20737 (89 x 233)

Dividing any number by the next one above it (except very early in the sequence) will give almost the same answer for any pair. This fraction, which increasingly approaches 0.618 the larger the numbers become, is known as the Golden Section. The Golden Ratio (approximately 1.61) is found by dividing any number in the sequence by the one immediately before it (eg. 13 ÷ 8) and describes the proportions of the Golden Rectangle.

When finding the differences between each pair of adjacent numbers, an identical sequence is generated. Pupils should be able to offer some kind of explanation based on the fact that since the original sequence is generated by **adding** adjacent numbers, then the sequence generated by **subtracting** them must be the same.

8. Strange snooker

This is a 5 x 4 snooker table with a pocket at each corner:

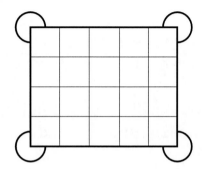

A snooker ball is launched from the corner marked A on a path that is at 45°
to the sides of the table. Every time it hits a cushion it rebounds making a
90° turn. It continues to bounce around the table in this way until it drops
into a pocket. On the 5 x 4 table the path of the ball would look like this:

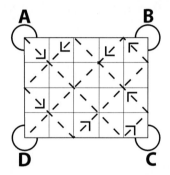

Counting the launch from corner A as one bounce, each rebound from a
cushion as one bounce, and the final pocket as one bounce this makes 9
bounces before dropping into pocket D.

This is how a ball behaves on a 6 x 4 table.

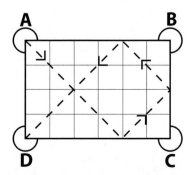

Investigate the paths of balls on tables of different sizes.

8. Strange snooker

Challenges for pupils

- Try to find a connection between the dimensions of the table (length and breadth), the number of bounces and the final pocket.

- See if you can use this connection to predict how many bounces a ball will make if you know the length and breadth of the table.

- Look at the patterns made by the pathways of the balls. Can you find which sizes of tables give the same pathway patterns? Can you explain why some of these patterns are created? (Clue: try tables measuring 2 x 1, 4 x 2, 6 x 3 etc. first.)

- Use everything you have learned from this investigation to work out the answer to the following question:

  Starting with a table measuring 48 x 42, how many bounces will the ball make, which pocket will it land in and what pattern will its pathway make?

  Explain how you know.

8. Strange snooker

Solutions

The number of bounces that a ball will make is derived from the ratio of the length to the breadth of the table, expressed in its lowest terms. For example:

- A table measuring 5 x 4 (that is, the ratio of the length to the breadth is 5:4) will cause the ball to bounce 9 times (5 + 4).

- Tables measuring 10 x 8 and 15 x 12 etc. will also cause the ball to bounce 9 times (ratios of 10:8 and 15:12 both reduce to 5:4).

- Tables measuring 2 x 1, 4 x 2, 6 x 3 etc. will all cause the ball to bounce 3 times (2 + 1).

- Any table whose length and breadth are in the ratio 3:2 (3 x 2, 6 x 4, 9 x 6 etc.) will give 5 bounces (3 + 2).

There are also similarities and differences in the pathways of the balls - all tables having the same ratio of length to breadth will show the same pattern, but there is a difference between the pattern on a 6 x 4 (3:2) table and a 5 x 4 (5:4) table for example.

9. Number chains

To make a number chain you must follow these rules:

- Start with any number

- Multiply the units digit by four and add the tens digit

Examples:

6 ⇨ 24 ⇨ 18 ⇨ 33 ⇨ 15 ⇨ 21 ⇨ 6

14 ⇨ 17 ⇨ 29 ⇨ 38 ⇨ 35 ⇨ 23 ⇨ 14

Both of these number chains come back to the starting number. Does this happen with all start numbers? Try starting with some bigger numbers like 56 or 48, as well as smaller numbers.

Investigate number chains with this rule.

9. Number chains

Challenges for pupils

• Can you make a number chain for each number from 1 to 50? Work systematically starting with 1 and you will find you don't need to work them all out. Can you say why?

• Which numbers do not come back to the number you started with? Can you explain why?

• Try to make some general statements about these number chains.

• There are 3 numbers between 1 and 50 that will not make chains at all. Can you find them? Which other numbers up to 100 will not make chains? Can you make a general statement about numbers that will not 'chain'?

• Look at the second number in each chain for the numbers 1-20 and write them out in order. What do you notice?

• Do the same with the last number in each chain (before getting back to the start number). What do you notice?

• Make up another rule for making number chains and investigate in the same way.

9. Number chains

Solutions and notes

Not all start numbers will form a complete loop, starting and ending with the same number.

For example:

$56 \Rightarrow 29 \Rightarrow 38 \Rightarrow 35 \Rightarrow 23 \Rightarrow 14 \Rightarrow 17 \Rightarrow 29$ which returns to the second number in the chain and creates an 'internal' loop.

The same thing happens with 48:

$48 \Rightarrow 36 \Rightarrow 27 \Rightarrow 30 \Rightarrow 3 \Rightarrow 12 \Rightarrow 9 \Rightarrow 36$ etc.

Having written out the chains for all the numbers to 20 it is not necessary to make any more, as all numbers from 20 to 38 already appear in another chain, for example:

The chain for 3 is $3 \Rightarrow 12 \Rightarrow 9 \Rightarrow 36 \Rightarrow 27 \Rightarrow 30 \Rightarrow 3$ and contains the numbers 27, 30 and 36. The chain for each of these numbers is therefore the same as the chain for 3 but with a different starting point.

The numbers 13, 26 and 39 will not chain:

$13 \Rightarrow 13$, $26 \Rightarrow 26$, $39 \Rightarrow 39$

Other multiples of 13 are also problematical:

$52 \Rightarrow 13$, $65 \Rightarrow 26$, $78 \Rightarrow 39$, $91 \Rightarrow 13$ etc.

Numbers from 40 to 50 form 'internal' loops as their chains contain a number from 1 to 20 and will therefore always loop back to that number, for example the chain for 45 starts:

$45 \Rightarrow 24 \Rightarrow 18$

and then follows the 18 chain back to 18.

9. Number chains

Solutions and notes (continued)

The second numbers in each of the chains for 1 to 20 show patterns in which the numbers increase by 4 each time (chains for 1 to 9 have as their second numbers 4, 8, 12, 16, 20, 24, 28, 32, 36 and the chains for 10 to 19 have as their second numbers 1, 5, 9, (13), 17, 21, 25, 29, 33, 37).

The last number in each of the chains for 1 to 20 (before returning to the start number) show patterns involving an increase of 10 each time. (10, 20, 30, 1, 11, 21, 31, 2, 12, 22, 32, 3, (13), 23, 33, 4, 14, 24, 34).

Other rules to try for making chains could be, for example:

- Square the units digit and add the tens digit;

- For each number in the sequence: if it's even, halve it, if it's odd treble it and add one.

Pupils should make up their own rules and try them. Some rules will create chains and patterns, others will not.

10. Sprouts

This is an investigation involving spots and lines (or nodes and arcs).
Start with two spots on a piece of paper:

You must draw a line that starts at a spot and ends at a spot (not necessarily
a different one). So three possibilities would be:

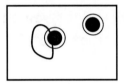 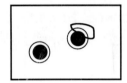 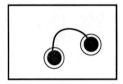

Whichever alternative you choose you must always draw a new spot on the line
you create. So, you would create one of these three possible drawings:

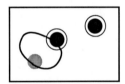 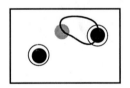 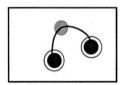

Continue to draw lines that start at a spot and end at a spot, always putting a
new spot on the line you draw. BUT:
   • A spot can no longer be used when it has three lines attached to it.
   • You may not draw a line so that it crosses another line.
There are three possible ways of building up your 'sprout':

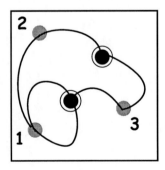 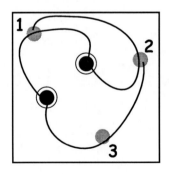 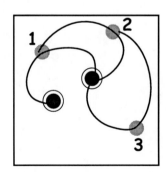

These are 'sprouts' that break the rules:

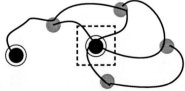 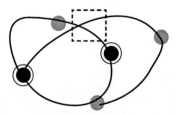

Start with different numbers of spots and explore the sprouts you can make.

10. Sprouts

Challenges for pupils

- When you have learned how to build sprouts, start keeping a record of the number of spots you start with and the number of lines you are able to draw before all the spots are used up.

- Can you use what you have learned to predict how many lines you can draw if you start with 10 spots? 20 spots? Any number of spots?

- Explain anything else you have found out whilst you have been investigating sprouts.

10. Sprouts

Solutions and notes

There is a relationship between the number of starting spots and the number of lines that can be drawn. Pupils attempting the challenges should be encouraged to record their findings in a table:

No. of spots (S)	No. of lines (L)
1	2
2	5
3	8
4	11

Using this table and looking closely at their drawings, they should be able to reach the generalisation: number of lines = 3 x number of spots minus 1 ($L = 3S - 1$). This can be explained by the fact that each spot on a completed sprout has 3 lines connected to it except the last one, which has only 2.

Pupils should also be able to comment on the fact that a completed sprout will have a greater number of lines if each new one is drawn round the outside of the existing ones, rather than within an enclosed region.

This

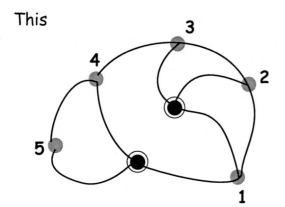

is more productive than this

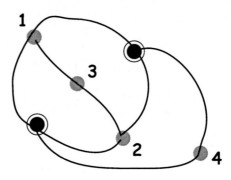

because 3 and 4 cannot be joined.

11. Consecutive sums

Is it possible to write every number as the sum of two or more consecutive numbers?

For example:

$$25 = 12 + 13$$
$$9 = 2 + 3 + 4$$
$$17 = 8 + 9$$
$$26 = 5 + 6 + 7 + 8$$

Which numbers up to 50 do you think can be written in this way?

Investigate.

11. Consecutive sums

Challenges for pupils

- Some numbers cannot be written as the sum of two or more consecutive numbers *(consecutive sums)*. Find out which numbers they are. What can you say about these numbers?
- As you explore, keep a note of which numbers can be made by adding two consecutive numbers together, which can be made by adding three consecutive numbers together and so on.
- Which numbers can be made in more than one way?
- What can you say about the numbers that can be made by adding two consecutive numbers together? *(They are the odd numbers; they go up in twos.)*
- What about the numbers that can be made by adding three consecutive numbers together? *(They are all numbers in the three times table; they go up in threes.)*
- And the numbers that can be made by adding four consecutive numbers together? *(They go up in fours but are not numbers in the four times table.)*
- Use what you have learned up to now to predict what you will find about the numbers that can be made by adding five consecutive numbers together, six, seven and so on. *(Those made by adding six consecutive numbers together go up in sixes, adding seven together gives a pattern of increasing by seven and so on.)*
- Look at all the numbers that are made by adding together consecutive numbers starting with 1 + ...:

    1 + 2
    1 + 2 + 3
    1 + 2 + 3 + 4 etc.

    What can you say about these numbers? *(They are triangular numbers.)*
- Investigate the sums of consecutive odd numbers (1 + 3, 3 + 5, 1 + 3 + 5 etc.)
- Investigate the sums of consecutive even numbers (2 + 4, 4 + 6, 2 + 4 + 6 etc.)
- Can some numbers be expressed as the sum of both consecutive odd numbers and consecutive even numbers? *(Yes, for example 12 can be written as 5 + 7 and as 2 + 4 + 6.)*

11. Consecutive sums

Solutions

It is possible to express most numbers as the sum of two or more consecutive numbers. Some numbers can be expressed as consecutive sums in more than one way. The exceptions are the powers of 2, -2, 4, 8, 16, 32, 64 etc. which cannot be expressed as consecutive sums.

Pupils should be encouraged, after an initial period of free exploration, to approach this problem, not by starting at 1, then 2 then 3 etc, which can become very tedious and frustrating, but by listing pairs of consecutive numbers and their totals:

1 + 2 = 3
2 + 3 = 5
3 + 4 = 7

This leads on to listing trios of numbers:

1 + 2 + 3 = 6
2 + 3 + 4 = 9

Then on to sets of 4:

1 + 2 + 3 + 4 = 10

and so on.

12. Pentominoes

Pentominoes are shapes made up of 5 squares joined together edge to edge.
There are twelve different ways of arranging 5 squares to make this set of
pentominoes (reflections and rotations are not counted).

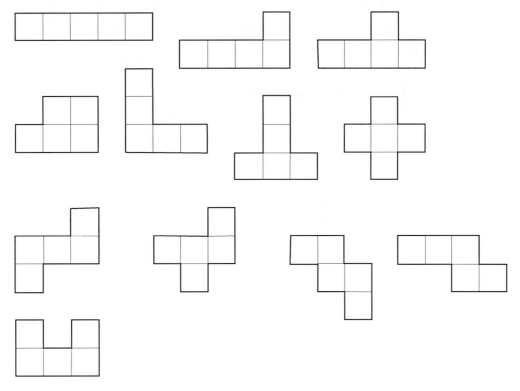

These two pentomino shapes are similar. That means that they are exactly
the same shape but different sizes. The bigger one is made using 4 other
pentominoes as shown and is twice as wide as the smaller one.

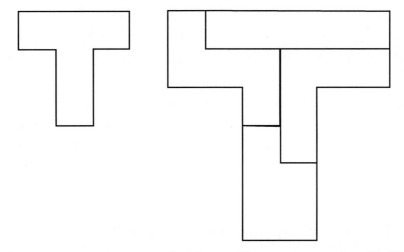

Explore the other pentominoes to find out if you can make double-sized
copies of them all.

12. Pentominoes

Challenges for pupils

- Choose a pentomino. Use any 9 of the others to form a large scale model of the one you have chosen. It will be three times as wide as the smaller one.

- Can you do this for every pentomino?

- Make any shape you like by fitting two pentominoes together like jigsaw pieces. Use any two **other** pentominoes to make a congruent shape (identical in both shape and size). Now try to fit **the remaining** 8 pentominoes together to make the same shape again, but this time it will be twice as long and twice as wide as the other two. (You will now have used all the twelve pentominoes.)

Try this one first:

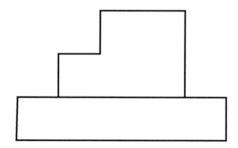

- Can you do this with other shapes made out of 2 pentominoes?

- It is possible to fit all the pentominoes together, like a jigsaw, to make a rectangle measuring 10 x 6. There are 2339 different ways of doing it! Are you brave enough to try to find one of them?

12. Pentominoes

Some Solutions

Larger Model

Congruent and Similar

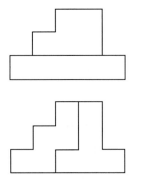

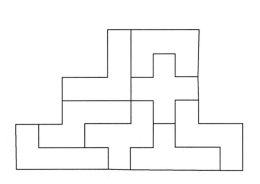

Similar Pairs

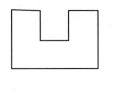

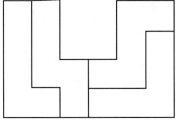

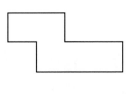

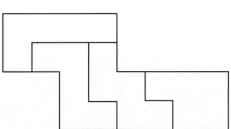

12. Pentominoes

13. Fours galore

Using four 4s and the operations + x - ÷ √ in any combination, how many different answers can you make?

The rules are:

- You must use exactly four 4s in each calculation and no other number.

- You may use any number of the operations signs in any combination, in each calculation.

- You may use brackets.

- All calculations must be mathematically correct and understandable to the reader.
  (For example, 4 + 4 x 4 - 4 could make 28, 16 or 0 depending on the order of operation. The reader might calculate:

  (4 + 4) x 4 - 4 = 28   or
  4 + (4 x 4) - 4 = 16   or even
  (4 + 4) x (4 - 4) = 0

  So the brackets are an important part of the calculation.)

These are some examples (some are very simple, some more complicated):

4 + 4 + 4 + 4 = 16
(4 - √4) x (4 x 4) = 32
444 - 4 = 440
(4 ÷ 4) + 4 - 4 = 1
(44 ÷ 4) + 4 = 15

Make up more calculations using four 4s. You may use a calculator to help you.

13. Fours galore

Challenges for pupils

- Can you make up a calculation for every number from 1 to 24? Here are a few to start you off:

    $$1 = (4 + 4 - 4) \div 4$$
    $$2 = (4 \div 4) + (4 \div 4)$$
    $$3 = (4 + 4 + 4) \div 4$$
    $$4 = (\sqrt{4} + \sqrt{4}) + (4 - 4)$$

Handy hint:

Remember that $\sqrt{4}$ is 2 and that $(4 \div 4)$ is 1. If you see $\sqrt{4}$ you still have three fours left to use and if you use $(4 \div 4)$ you have two fours left. Another useful tool is $(4 - 4)$ which, in some calculations, allows you to use up all your fours without changing the answer.

- What's the biggest number you can make using four 4s?

- Try the same investigations but using four different numbers, perhaps 1, 2, 3 and 4. With these numbers you might make:

    $$1 + 2 + 3 + 4 = 10$$
    $$(3 \times 4) - (1 + 2) = 9$$

or perhaps you could use the two in a different way:

$$4^2 + 3 - 1 = 18$$

Handy hint:

Any number divided by 1 or multiplied by 1 remains unchanged.

13. Fours galore

Notes

Any calculation that is correct and complies with the rules can be accepted. Pupils might be asked to explain some of their calculations to establish whether or not they understand order of operations and the significance of brackets.

Some pupils may be able enough to consider using 4 to represent the power of 4, as in $4^4 = 256$, when investigating the biggest number they can make. It may also be appropriate for some pupils to investigate the involvement of negative numbers.

14. Spotty shapes

Using a 4 x 4 spotty grid, or a 4 x 4 pin board, make some shapes with no spots inside, like these:

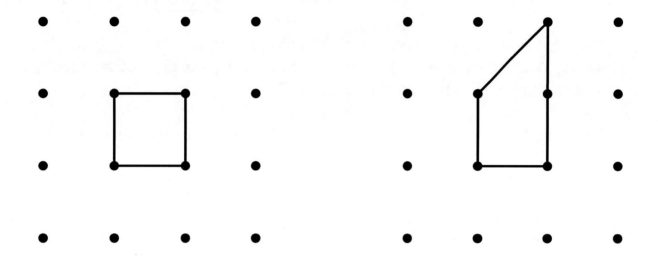

All the shapes must be made up of whole and half squares.

How many different shapes can you make?

Work out the area of each shape and count the number of spots on its perimeter.

What is the largest shape you can make - that is, the one with the largest number of spots on its perimeter? Does this shape also have the largest area?

Be sure to keep a record of all the shapes that you make and everything you find out.

14. Spotty shapes

Challenges for pupils

• Look at all your shapes. What happens to the area of a shape as you increase the number of spots on its perimeter? Can you predict what the area would be of a shape with 20 spots on its perimeter? With 50 spots? Can you make up a general rule connecting the area of a shape to the number of spots on its perimeter?

• Investigate shapes with one spot inside, like these, in the same way:

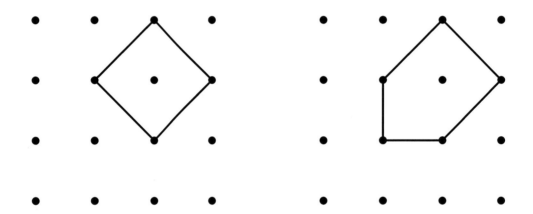

Keep a record of the area and the number of spots on the perimeter of each shape you make. Does the area grow in the same way? Is the rule connecting the area and the number of perimeter spots still the same or has it changed?

• Try the investigation again with shapes having two spots inside. What do you think you will find out this time? (Make predictions before you start, and then check them out as you work.)

• If you were to make shapes with three spots inside what would you find out? What would you find out about shapes having five spots inside? Can you make a general rule for any number of spots inside?

14. Spotty shapes

Solutions

Pupils should be encouraged to record their findings in a table:

No. of spots on perimeter (p)	Area (a)
3	$\frac{1}{2}$
4	1
5	$1\frac{1}{2}$
6	2
7	$2\frac{1}{2}$
8	3

This should lead to the generalisations:

- The area grows by half a square each time an additional spot is used in the perimeter.
- $a = (p \div 2) - 1$

The rule for shapes with:

- one spot inside $a = p \div 2$
- two spots inside $a = (p \div 2) + 1$
- three spots inside $a = (p \div 2) + 2$
- five spots inside $a = (p \div 2) + 4$

In all cases the area grows by half a square each time a perimeter spot is added.

Some pupils may be able to generalise that the area will always grow by half a square as perimeter spots are added, and the rule is that the area is always half the number of perimeter spots plus a number that is one less than the number of spots inside. This rule holds true in all cases - for the shapes having no spots inside the area is half the number of perimeter spots plus one less than zero (which is the same as subtract one).

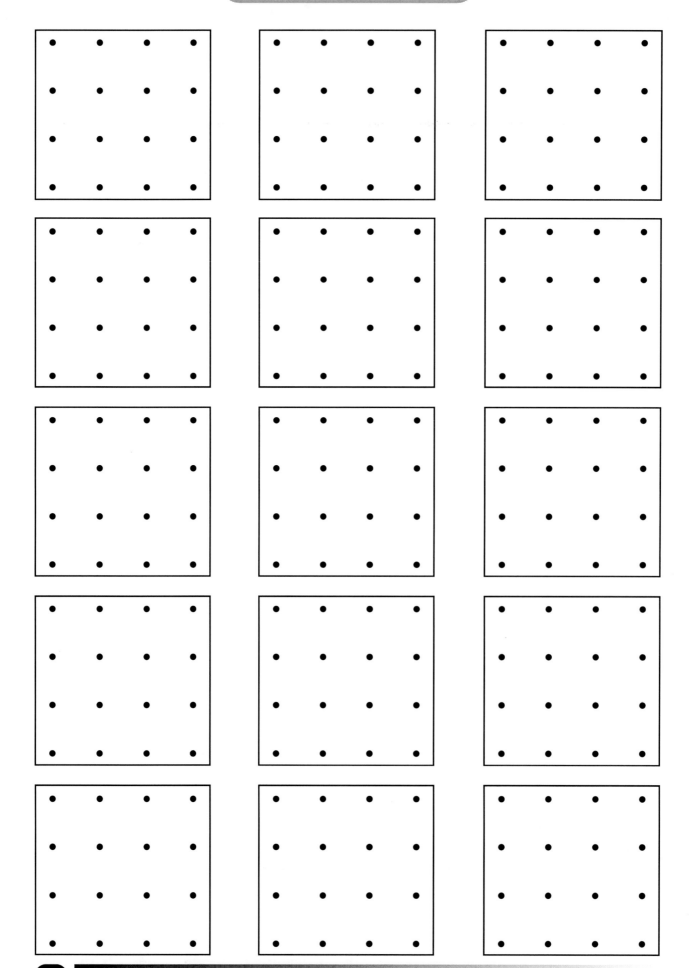

15. Twelve days of Christmas

Find a copy of the words for the song 'Twelve days of Christmas'.

How many presents altogether were sent on the first day, the second day, the third day and so on? (Remember that on the second day the presents sent were 'two turtle doves and a partridge in a pear tree' 3 in all.)

How many of each present were sent? (How many turtle doves, how many partridges etc.)

How many presents were sent altogether in the twelve days?

How many legs were sent altogether? How many arms? How many wings?

15. Twelve days of Christmas

Challenges for pupils

- What other things in the rhyme might you count, for example drumsticks, milking stools? How many of each of these things would have been sent each day, and how many altogether in all 12 days?

- If presents had continued arriving in the same pattern, how many would have been sent on the 13th day?

- How many would have been sent on the 20th day? On the 100th day? Can you find a way of working this out without having to do a long addition?

- How many presents would be sent on the nth day?

15. Twelve days of Christmas

Solutions

Day No.	Present type	No. of presents per day	No. of presents each type	Legs	Arms	Wings
1	Partridge in a pear tree	1	12	24		24
2	Turtle doves	3	22	44		44
3	French hens	6	30	60		60
4	Calling birds	10	36	72		72
5	Gold rings	15	40			
6	Geese a-laying	21	42	84		84
7	Swans a-swimming	28	42	84		84
8	Maids a-milking	36	40	80	80	
9	Ladies dancing	45	36	72	72	
10	Lords a-leaping	55	30	60	60	
11	Pipers piping	66	22	44	44	
12	Drummers drumming	78	12	24	24	
	TOTALS	**364**	**364**	**648**	**280**	**368**

On the 13th day there would have been 91 presents sent. $\frac{1}{2}$ *(13 x 14)*

On the 20th day there would have been 210. $\frac{1}{2}$ *(20 x 21)*

On the 100th day the number would have been 5 050. $\frac{1}{2}$ *(100 x 101)*

On the nth day the number of presents is calculated as $\dfrac{n \times (n+1)}{2}$

Pupils may recognise that these are triangular numbers.

16. Box clever

Use sheets of card measuring 15 cm by 15 cm to make boxes without lids. Do this by cutting squares out of each corner and then folding up the sides.

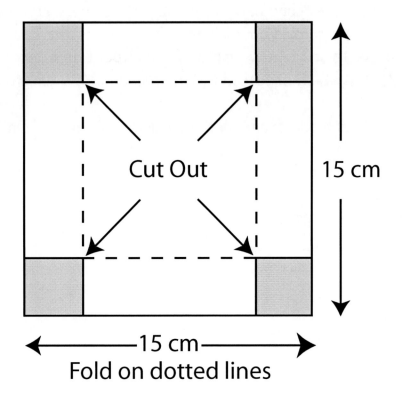

Cut Out

15 cm

←——15 cm——→

Fold on dotted lines

The squares you cut out must have sides measuring whole centimetres - fractions of centimetres or millimetres, are not allowed.

What is the largest box you can make in this way (that is, the one with the greatest volume)?

What other volumes can you create?

16. Box clever

Challenges for pupils

- Work out the area of card used to make each box. Are there any boxes that have a volume that is numerically the same as the area of card needed to make them? (An example of this would be a box with a volume of 79 cm^3 which used card with an area of 79 cm^2 to make it.)

- Investigate boxes made from card measuring 20cm x 20cm (400 cm^2).

- Will you get the same results or different ones if you investigate boxes made from card measuring 25 cm x 16 cm (which has the same area as the 20 cm x 20 cm card)?

16. Box clever

Solutions

- The greatest volume is created by cutting out a square measuring 3 cm x 3 cm from each corner. This gives a volume of 243 cm^3.

  Other volumes that can be created are:

  169 cm^3 by cutting out 1 cm x 1 cm corners
  242 cm^3 by cutting out 2 cm x 2 cm corners
  196 cm^3 by cutting out 4 cm x 4 cm corners
  125 cm^3 by cutting out 5 cm x 5 cm corners
  54 cm^3 by cutting out 6 cm x 6 cm corners
  7 cm^3 by cutting out 7 cm x 7 cm corners

The box with a volume of 125cm^3 uses card with an area of 125cm^2.

The volumes which can be created from card measuring 20 cm x 20 cm are (in cm^3):

324, 512, 588, 576, 500, 384, 252, 128 and 36

The volumes which can be created from card measuring 25 cm x 16 cm are (in cm^3):

322, 504, 570, 544, 540, 312 and 154

None of these boxes has a volume that is numerically the same as the area of the card used to make them.

17. Lucky seven

How many three digit numbers are there that contain at least one 7?

How many of these contain just one 7?

How many contain exactly two 7s?

How many start with a 7?

How many end with a 7?

How many have 7 in the middle position?

How many both start and end with a 7?

17. Lucky seven

Challenges for pupils

- Use what you have learned to explore 7s in four digit numbers.

- How many three digit numbers contain **only** odd numbers? (Don't count any with zeros in them, such as 305, 350.)

- Are there the same number of three digit numbers containing **only** even numbers? *(Don't count any with zeros in them such as 402, 420 etc.)*

17. Lucky seven

Solutions

252 numbers contain at least one 7
225 numbers contain just one 7
26 numbers contain exactly two 7s
100 numbers start with 7 (including those with 7s in other positions)
90 numbers end with 7 (including those with 7s in other positions)
90 numbers have 7 in the middle position (including those with 7s in other positions)
10 numbers both start and end with 7 (including 777)

There are 125 three digit numbers containing only odd numbers (any numbers with zeros in any position are not allowed).

Excluding any numbers containing zero in any position, there are 64 three digit numbers containing only even numbers.

It may be appropriate to discuss with pupils why zero has not been allowed in the count: both odd and even numbers are defined as non-zero integers. Zero is a place holder within other numbers.

18. Chess board squares

A chess board is made up of 64 small squares - but how many squares has it really got?

It has 64 small squares but it also has one big square - the board itself!

And what about all those squares made up of four of the smaller ones?

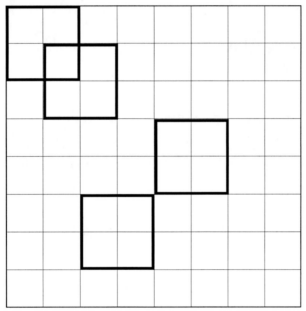

Some squares are made up of 9 of the smaller ones.

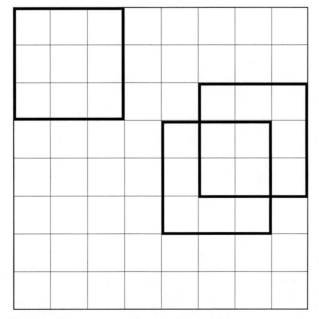

How many squares altogether on a chess board?

18. Chess board squares

Challenges for pupils

- How many squares on a 3 x 3 board, on a 4 x 4 board etc.?

- How many squares would there be on a 10 x 10 board? On a 12 x 12 board? You should be able to work out these answers from what you have learned.

- Can you make a general rule that will allow you to work out how many squares on any size of board?

- Start with a 4 x 4 board. How many rectangles (that are not squares) can you find on the board? Count each rectangle both ways - count 2 x 1 rectangles as well as 1 x 2 rectangles, for example. Make sure you find all possible sizes of rectangles in all possible positions.

- Do the same thing with larger boards.

18. Chess board squares

Solutions and notes

Some pupils might find it easier to start with smaller 'chess boards' first - boards made up of 9 small squares, 16 small squares, 25 small squares etc. and build up to the 8 x 8 chess board. In this case some of the 'challenges for pupils' will already have been covered.

On the 8 x 8 chess board there are 204 squares in total, made up in the following way:

Size of square	No. of squares
8 x 8	1
7 x 7	4
6 x 6	9
5 x 5	16
4 x 4	25
3 x 3	36
2 x 2	49
1 x 1	64

To generalise, on an 8 x8 board there are $1^2 + 2^2 + 3^2 + 4^2 + 5^2 + 6^2 + 7^2 + 8^2$
On an n x n board there are $1^2 + 2^2 + 3^2 +$ .... n^2 squares.

On a 4 x 4 board there are 70 rectangles that are not squares:

    24 measuring 1 x 2 and 2 x 1
    16 measuring 1 x 3 and 3 x 1
     8 measuring 1 x 4 and 4 x 1
    12 measuring 2 x 3 and 3 x 2
     6 measuring 2 x 4 and 4 x 2
     4 measuring 3 x 4 and 4 x 3

19. Games of patience

Game 1

Use one red suit and one black suit from a pack of cards (including picture cards but no jokers).

Make a number line with all the black cards, starting with the ace which represents one, and ending with the picture cards with the Jack representing 11, the Queen representing 12 the King representing 13.

Your task is to place each red card on one of the black cards so that the pair together total a square number. For example, you could place a red 3 on top of a black ace to make 4, and a red 9 on top of a black 7 to make 16. Your task is complete when every red card has been placed on top of a black, and all 13 pairs make square numbers.

Is this the only way to do it? Give reasons for your answer.

Game 2

You need a pack of cards with the picture cards and the jokers removed. Shuffle the cards, take the top 6 and place them in a line which will form the base of a pyramid. Your pyramid when complete will look like this:

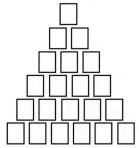

All six cards must have different values so if any two or more are the same place duplicates back in the pack and choose different ones.

Put the rest of the cards face down in a pile. Take the top card, turn it over, and see whether its value is the same as the sum of, or difference between, any two adjacent numbers in the base of the pyramid. If it is, place the card above them, if not, discard it. Go on building in this way until the pyramid is complete. If you run out of cards, turn over the discarded pile and use that.

Can you always complete a pyramid?

19. Games of patience

Challenges for pupils

Game 1

- Try the same task again, but this time with the ace having a value of 14 rather than 1. Can you still make all the pairs add up to square numbers?

- Use only the cards from ace (1) to Queen (12). Can you still pair all the cards to make square numbers? *(Yes, as for the previous challenge in which 14 was the highest number, but with 1/3, 2/2 and 3/1 pairings replacing the A/2, 2/A and K/3, 3/K pairings.)*

Game 2

- Try the game again, this time using all the cards in the pack (except the jokers). The values of the picture cards are 11 for the Jack, 12 for the Queen and 13 for the King.

19. Games of patience

Solutions and notes

Game 1

The pairings that give square numbers are:
A/8, 2/2, 3/K, 4/Q, 5/J, 6/10, 7/9, 8/A, 9/7, 10/6, J/5, Q/4, K/3

This is the only solution because the 9, 10 and Jack can only be made up to 16 as there is no card with a high enough value to make them up to the next square number, 25. Once the position of these cards is fixed the position of all the others is fixed: for example, the 2 can only be partnered by 2 or 7 but the 7 is fixed. Therefore the 2 must be partnered by 2 etc.

The pairings when the Ace is counted as 14 are:
2/A, 3/K, 4/Q, 5/J, 6/10, 7/9, 8/8, 9/7, 10/6, J/5, Q/4, K/3, A/2

Game 2

There are many possible pyramids depending on the cards in the base and the order in which cards are drawn from the pack. It is not necessarily possible to always complete a pyramid once started, again depending on the order in which numbers are drawn.

This is an example of the numbers in a completed pyramid.

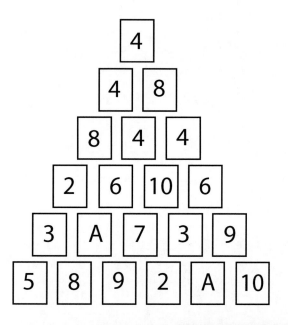

20. Consecutive totals

Choose any three consecutive numbers, for example 16, 17 and 18. Add them together and write down the total.

Choose three more consecutive numbers and write down their total.

Repeat with several more trios of consecutive numbers.

What can you say about the totals?

Explain why this happens.

20. Consecutive totals

Challenges for pupils

- Try trios of three consecutive even numbers (e.g. 12, 14, 16). What can you say about their totals? *(Multiple of 3, three times middle number, always even.)*
- Try trios of three odd numbers. What can you say about their totals? *(Multiple of 3, three times the middle number, always odd.)*
- Make up your own rules for trios of numbers and see what you can find out. *(Provided that the difference between the smallest and the middle numbers and the middle and largest numbers is the same, the total will always be a multiple of three that is three times the middle number. The middle number determines whether it is odd or even. For example 10, 23 and 36 total to 69 (3 x 23). The total is odd because 23 is odd.)*
- Use what you have learned to answer questions like these and explain how you found the answers:
    - Three consecutive numbers have a total of 771. What are they? *(256, 257, 258 found by dividing 771 by 3 which gives 257, the middle number of the three.)*
    - The total of 3 consecutive multiples of 3 is 576. What are the numbers? *(189, 192, 195 found by dividing 576 by 3 to give the middle number 192. As they are consecutive multiples of three the other numbers must be three less and three more than 192.)*
- Make up some questions like these for someone else to answer.
- What would you expect to find if you added together five consecutive numbers? *(The total is a multiple of 5, is five times the middle number and whether it is odd or even is determined by the middle number.)*
- Try sets of 5 consecutive odd/even numbers, multiples of three etc. Explain what you find.
- Can you say what the rules would be for sets of seven consecutive numbers/odd numbers/even numbers/multiples of 10 etc.?
- Use everything you have been working on to help you to explore sets of 4 consecutive numbers, 6 consecutive numbers, 8 consecutive numbers etc. *(These do not have a middle number!) (All the rules still apply, but the 'working' number is the mean of the two middle numbers, e.g. the total of 7, 8, 9, 10 is 34, which is 4 x 8.5, 8.5 being the mean of 8 and 9. Totals of 4, 6, 8 etc. consecutive numbers will always be even as they involve multiplying by 4. E.g. the total of 3, 6, 9, 12 is 30, which is 4 times 7.5 (the mean of 6 and 9).*

20. Consecutive totals

Solutions

The sum of any three consecutive numbers will always be:
- a multiple of 3,
- three times the middle number,
- odd if the middle number is odd,
- even if the middle number is even.

Any explanation that is correct should be accepted. The algebraic generalisation is:

$$n + (n+1) + (n+2) = 3n + 3 \text{ or}$$
$$(n-1) + n + (n+1) = 3n$$

Both these algebraic expressions show that the total must be a multiple of 3.

To show whether the total is odd or even:

$$O + E + O = E \text{ because } (O+O) = E \text{ and then } E + E = E$$
$$E + O + E = O \text{ because } (E+E) = E \text{ and then } E + O = O$$

All trios of consecutive numbers are either O, E, O or E, O, E

21. One-line shapes

Can you make a copy of this drawing by following two simple rules:

- You must not lift your pencil from the paper once you have started drawing (in other words the drawing must be made of one continuous pencil line).
- You must not retrace a line you have already drawn, although you may cross other lines.

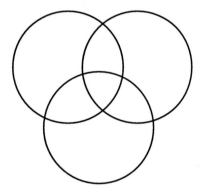

Now try the same thing with these circles:

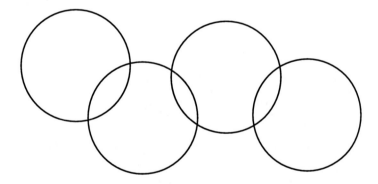

And finally, try the Olympic flag:

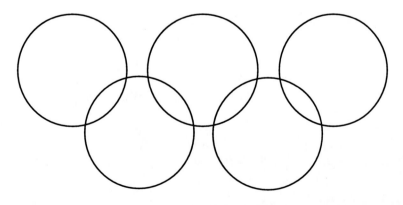

21. One-line shapes

Challenges for pupils

• Which of these drawings can you make with one continuous pencil line, according to the rules?

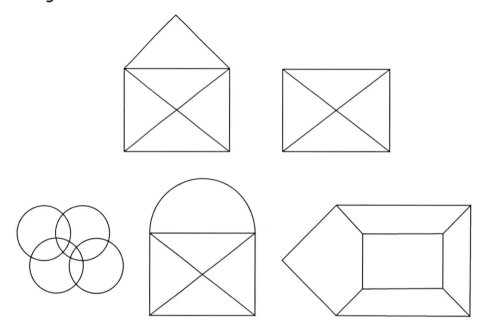

• What can you say about drawings that can and cannot be made with one continuous pencil line?

> Hint: It has something to do with **nodes**. Nodes are points with lines going to and from them.

This drawing has 6 nodes: This one has 5 nodes:

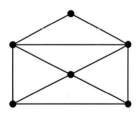   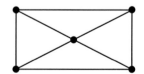

You need to look at whether nodes are odd (have an odd number of lines going in and out of them) or even (have an even number of lines going in and out of them).

• Experiment with drawings of your own.

21. One-line shapes

Solutions

The three-circle drawing can be completed in this way (there are other ways):

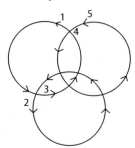

Once the strategy of tracing round the outside of most of the drawing first is established, it will work for any of the circle drawings.

In general, if a drawing has **no more than two** points (nodes) with an **odd** number of lines radiating from them (known as odd nodes), it can be drawn with one continuous pencil line. It makes no difference whether the lines are straight or curved:

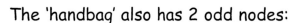

This 'open envelope' has 2 odd nodes: The 'handbag' also has 2 odd nodes:

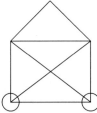   

Both can therefore be drawn with one continuous pencil line. The line starts at one odd node and ends at the other. (In a drawing with only one odd node, the line must **either** start **or** end at this node.)

The circle drawings in the original task have no odd nodes, which is why they can all be drawn with a continuous line. (The line can start at any point, and will end at the same one.)

The 'closed envelope' has 4 odd nodes:

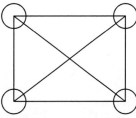

This cannot be drawn with one continuous pencil line.

22. Square away

Look at these calculations:

$$5^2 - 4^2 = 9$$
$$9^2 - 8^2 = 17$$
$$15^2 - 14^2 = 29$$

They all show the difference between the squares of consecutive numbers.

Make up some more calculations like these and write them down.

Can you see a quick way of finding the answers without using a calculator - even when the numbers are quite big like $37^2 - 36^2$?

Work out and write down the differences between the squares of all pairs of consecutive numbers from $2^2 - 1^2$ to $20^2 - 19^2$

Look at the way in which the answers grow when you put them in order. What can you say about the pattern?

22. Square away

Challenges for pupils

- Try the same things with calculations like these:

$$12^2 - 10^2 = 44$$
$$9^2 - 7^2 = 32$$

In these calculations the numbers being squared have a difference of 2.

- Now try the same things with calculations where the numbers being squared have a difference of 3:

$$13^2 - 10^2 = 69$$
$$10^2 - 7^2 = 51$$

- Can you make some predictions about what would happen if you tried numbers with a difference of 4, 5 etc.? Can you make a general rule for any numbers?

22. Square away

Solutions

Pupils should be encouraged to make the following generalisations:

The difference between the squares of a pair of consecutive numbers is equal to the sum of the numbers themselves:

$$5^2 - 4^2 = 5 + 4 = 9$$
$$37^2 - 36^2 = 37 + 36 = 73$$
$$a^2 - b^2 = a + b$$

When all the calculations are placed in order from $2^2 - 1^2 = 3$ to $20^2 - 19^2 = 39$ the answers are consecutive odd numbers (increasing by 2 - twice the difference between the numbers being squared):

$$3, 5, 7, 9 \; 11, 13, 15, 17, \ldots\ldots\ldots\ldots\ldots \; 39$$

Calculations for pairs of numbers with a difference of 2:

$$12^2 - 10^2 = 2 \times (12 + 10) = 44$$
$$9^2 - 7^2 = 2 \times (9 + 7) = 32$$
$$a^2 - b^2 = 2 (a + b)$$

If all the calculations are put in order the answers go up in 4s (twice the difference between the numbers being squared).

Likewise, if the numbers being squared have a difference of 3 then:

$$a^2 - b^2 = 3 \times (a + b)$$
and the answers go up by 6 each time (twice the difference between the numbers being squared).

In general:
* the answers are always found by multiplying the sum of the numbers being squared by their difference,
* when the calculations are arranged in order, the answers grow by twice the difference between the numbers being squared.

23. Half time

At the end of a game of football the score was 4 - 2. How many possible half time scores could there have been?

You will need to work systematically, recording all the possible scores as you find them.

Can you record all the possible scores in different ways?

What if the final score had been 4 - 3? Or 4 - 4?

What if, in a game of basketball, the final score had been 15 - 12. What would all the possible half time scores have been?

23. Half time

Challenges for pupils

* Can you work out a general rule that will tell you how many possible half time scores there are for any final score?

23. Half time

Solutions

Pupils should be encouraged to list their half time scores in a systematic way. One way might be:

0 - 0	0 - 1	0 - 2	4 - 0	3 - 0	2 - 0	1 - 0
	1 - 1	1 - 2	4 - 1	3 - 1	2 - 1	
		2 - 2	4 - 2	3 - 2		

However, a more useful way of recording is:

0 - 0	0 - 1	0 - 2 $\longrightarrow$ (n + 1)
1 - 0	1 - 1	1 - 2
2 - 0	2 - 1	2 - 2
3 - 0	3 - 1	3 - 2
4 - 0	4 - 1	4 - 2

(m + 1)

because this leads to the generalisation more readily:
- number of possible half time scores = $(m + 1)(n + 1)$
- where m and n are the full time scores for each team respectively.

24. Same but different

Start with a 3 digit number in which all the digits are different and there is no zero. Reverse the number and find the difference between them. Reverse your answer and add.

Examples:

Start Number	673	529 ⟶ 925
Reverse and find difference	-376	-529
Answer	297	396
Reverse and add	792	693
Answer	1089	1089

Try some other three digit numbers. What happens?
(If, when you have found the difference, you are left with 99, place a zero in front of it (099) before reversing and adding.)

What happens if some or all of the digits are the same in your starting number, for example 353, 299, 558, 777? Try some more numbers like these.

Will this still work if you use zeros in your numbers? Try zeros in different positions, for example 703, 380 (reverse to 083), 400 (reverse to 004). Try some more numbers like these.

24. Same but different

Challenges for pupils

* Try this method starting with two digit numbers. Remember to try those with a zero. What do you find?

* Try this method starting with four digit numbers. Remember to try these numbers with 4 different digits, numbers with some or all of the digits the same and numbers that have zeros. As with your three digit number investigation, make sure you include numbers with repeat digits in different positions and with zeros in different positions:

  For example, 8823, 8283, 8238, 2388, 2838 - do all these have the same outcome?
  Do all these have the same outcome - 2340, 2304, 2034?

* What about five digit numbers?

* Look back at your answers in all the work you have been doing. What do **all** of them have in common?

24. Same but different

Solutions and notes

Almost all three digit numbers treated in this way will always give the answer 1089. The exceptions are numbers such as 353 and 777 which, when reversed give the same number.

Four digit numbers generally give either 9999 or 10890 as the answer although there are occasional exceptions - 8328 for example will give 0990.

With five digit numbers the results are not quite as obvious, but most will give recognisable patterns in the digits of the answers. Many will result in 99099, some in 109890.

All start numbers with **any number** of digits will always give a multiple of 9 as the answer - all the digits in the answer will give 9 when added together. Example: The sum of the digits in 1089 is 18, the sum of the digits in 18 is 9

25. Multi-plications

Choose any four digits from 1 to 9. They must all be different.

How many different two digit by two digit multiplications can you make?
Write them all down.

Example:

> With 1, 2, 3 and 4 you could make 12 x 34, 23 x 14, 43 x 21 etc. (There
> are lots more to find, but make sure there are no repeats - 12 x 34 is
> the same as 34 x 12 in this investigation.)

Can you predict which one will give the largest answer and which will give the
smallest answer? You will need to work out some, or even all, of the
multiplications to check whether you are right.

Repeat with other sets of four digits, each time predicting and then checking
which multiplications will give the largest and smallest answers.

25. Multi-plications

Challenges for pupils

- Investigate what happens if, with your chosen four digits, you can also make three digit by one digit multiplications, for example 123 x 4. Will you have new largest and smallest answers or will they be the same?

- Investigate in the same way, multiplications made using five digits. This time your calculations could include, for example:

  1234 x 5 and 123 x 45

25. Multi-plications

Solutions and notes

Pupils should be encouraged to develop a system for finding all the possible two digit by two digit multiplications using the chosen four digits.

The complete set of possibilities for the digits 1, 2, 3 and 4 are:

12 x 34	12 x 43	21 x 34	21 x 43
13 x 24	13 x 42	31 x 24	31 x 42
14 x 23	14 x 32	41 x 23	41 x 32

The largest product is 1312 (41 x 32)

The smallest product is 312 (13 x 24)

The same patterns can be followed with other sets of four digits to find all possible multiplications and the largest and smallest answers.

The additional calculations that can be made (with 1, 2, 3 and 4) when three digit by one digit multiplications are allowed are:

123 x 4	132 x 4	213 x 4	231 x 4	312 x 4	321 x 4
124 x 3	142 x 3	214 x 3	241 x 3	412 x 3	421 x 3
134 x 2	143 x 2	314 x 2	341 x 2	413 x 2	431 x 2
234 x 1	243 x 1	324 x 1	342 x 1	423 x 1	432 x 1

The largest of these products is 1284 (321 x 4)

The smallest of these products is 234 (234 x 1)

26. Multiplication patterns

Multiply each of these numbers by 11, then by 111, then by 1111 and so on.
53, 45, 61, 13, 34, 32

Use a calculator and write down the answer each time.

Try some more two digit numbers whose digits add up to no more that 9 (e.g. 36, 25).

What do you notice?

Now try two digit numbers whose digits add up to more than 9 (e.g. 57, 68, 47 etc.)

Does the same thing happen?

Explain any patterns you find.

Try writing out the 11 times table, the 111 times table, the 1111 times table and so on (up to about 20 times the number each time). You should be able to see clear patterns developing.

Use these patterns to make predictions, for example, what the answer would be to 30 x 11 or 45 x 111 etc. Check all your predictions.

26. Multiplication patterns

Challenges for pupils

• Other interesting patterns are to be found by multiplying three digit numbers by 11, 111, 1111 etc.

• Or, try multiplying numbers by 11, then 101, 1001, 10001 etc. This works nicely with three digit numbers too.

• Now try to explain this:

> Start with a six digit number made up of three digits repeated:
> 458458
> Divide by 7, then 11 then 13
> The answer will be the orininal three digits
> 458
> This works with any number according to the rule.
> Why?

(In reverse, start with 458. Multiplying by 7, 11 and 13 is in effect multiplying by 1001. 1000 x 458 gives 458000, leaving 458 to add to give 458458)

• If you like elevens patterns try working out:
11 x 11
11 x 11 x 11
11 x 11 x 11 x 11
etc.

(You will find these numbers in Pascal's triangle if you look! You will find a copy of the triangle on page 18.)

26. Multiplication patterns

Solutions and notes

Some examples of numbers multiplied by 11, 111, 1111 etc. would be:
For 52 the answer are:

| 572 | 5772 | 57772 | 577772 |

When the digits in the number add up to more than 9 the pattern is different.
For 68 the answers are:

| 748 | 7548 | 75548 | 75548 |

The 11 times table up to 9 x 11 generates the numbers:
        11, 22, 33 etc, to 99.

All the answers are the number being multiplied by 11 written as both tens and units: 6 x 11 = 66.

Continuing to 18 x 11 the numbers generated are:
        110 , 121, 132, 143, 154, 165, 176, 187, 198.

The answers can be derived by writing down:
        The tens digit of the number being multiplied by 11, followed by the sum of the two digits, followed by the units digits, as in:

        15 x 11 = 165 made up of the 1 from the 15, followed by 6 (1 + 5) and finally the 5 from the 15.

At 19 x 11 this system appears to break down as 19 x 11 = 209.
However, following the process for 15 x 11 the answer to 19 x 11 would be
        1 (1 + 9) 9
        1 + 9 is 10, and in any addition calculation the 1 ten would be 'carried'
        If the 1 ten is 'carried' in the same way here it will be added to the
        first 1, becoming (1 + 1) 0 9 which gives 209.
This 'carrying' system can be used to explain all apparent breakdowns of patterns.

20 x 11 conforms to the original pattern to give 220.

Patterns in the 111 and the 1111 times tables can be explained using the same process.

27. Factor facts

To do this investigation you will first need to write out a list of factors for each number up to 50, like this:

1 ⟶ 1
2 ⟶ 1, 2
3 ⟶ 1, 3
4 ⟶ 1, 2, 4
and so on.

This is quite a big job!

Prime numbers have exactly two factors (which is why 1 is not a prime number!)

Investigate numbers which have exactly 3 factors (9 has exactly 3 factors, 1, 3 and 9). What can you say about these numbers? Check that you are correct by trying some more numbers, larger than 50, that you think will have exactly three factors.

What can you say about numbers that have an odd number of factors? Can you explain why they have an odd number of factors?

Look at numbers with exactly 4 factors. Do they have anything in common? And those with exactly 5 factors?

Explain anything else you find out about factors.

27. Factor facts

Challenges for pupils

• Investigate the factors of these numbers:
 2, 4, 8, 16, 38, 64, 128 ....

Start by deciding what you can say about these numbers. *(The most likely feature pupils will identify is that each one is double the last. They are, in fact, powers of 2: $2 = 2^1$, $4 = 2^2$, $8 = 2^3$, $16 = 2^4$ ....)*

Now list the factors of each number. What do you notice?
(The factors of each number are:
$2 \longrightarrow 1, 2$
$4 \longrightarrow 1, 2, 4$
$8 \longrightarrow 1, 2, 4, 8$
$16 \longrightarrow 1, 2, 4, 8, 16$
Each number has as its factors, all the factors of the number immediately before it plus itself.
Each number's factors show the same doubling pattern that is present in the numbers being investigated.
The number of factors is the 'power' number plus 1: 8 (2^3) has **4** *factors, the 'extra' factor being the 1.)*

• Try totalling each horizontal row of numbers in Pascal's triangle (on page 18). You might be surprised! *(The total of the first horizontal row, below the 1 at the top, is 2. The total of the next row is 4, then 8, then 116 and so on.)*

27. Factor facts

Solutions and notes

Squares of prime numbers have exactly 3 factors:

4, 9, 25, 49, 121, 169 etc.

All square numbers have an odd number of factors. Factors in all other numbers are in pairs, for example the factors of 12 are 1 and 12, 2 and 6, 3 and 4. However, square numbers are the product of multiplying a number by itself, thereby creating an odd number of factors:

The factors of 16 are 1 and 16, 2 and 8 and 4 to be squared.

In other explorations of factors, any explanation that makes sense and is not mathematically incorrect should be accepted. The purpose of this investigation is to focus pupils' attention on the properties of numbers whilst allowing them to be creative in their thinking.

28. Knight's move

In a game of chess the knight's move is either:

- two squares horizontally in either direction, followed by one square vertically in either direction (or the other way round).
- two squares vertically in either direction, followed by one square horizontally in either direction (or the other way round).

Examples of moves:

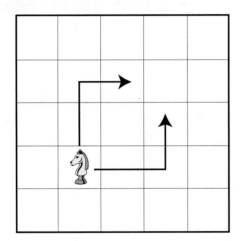 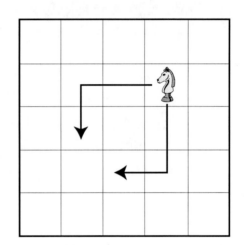

On the 25 square chess board below, how many different moves can the knight make from his centre position as shown?

How many different squares can he reach?

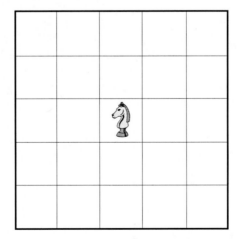

How many moves can he make and how many squares can he reach starting from all the other squares? For example, starting in a corner, starting in a square on an edge etc. Explain what you find.

28. Knight's move

Challenges for pupils

- Use what you have learned and found out to investigate moves on a 36 square chess board in the same way.

- If you like the knight's move problems try these:

  - Investigate the knight's move on boards of other sizes (smaller ones as well as larger ones).

  - Try a very old problem called 'Knight's Tour'. Can you move the knight around the board (according to the rules for a knight's move) so that you visit each square once and only once? If the 'tour' starts and ends at the same square it's called a 'Closed Tour' and is very difficult!

28. Knight's move

Solutions and notes

There are 16 possible moves from the centre position, and 8 squares that can be reached.

From each corner position there are only 4 possible moves, and 2 squares that can be reached.

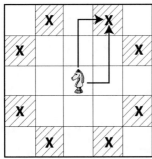

FROM CENTRE POSITION

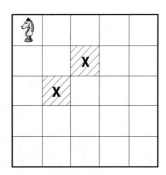

FROM EACH CORNER

(Each square can be reached by two different moves as shown.)

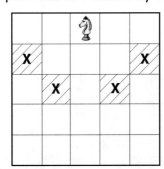

FROM CENTRE EDGE SQUARES

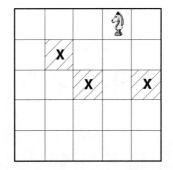

FROM OTHER EDGE SQUARES

All moves from all squares can be found by 'shifting' the board around the centre knight in such a way as to place the knight in the square being investigated:

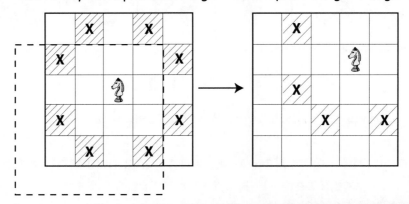

28. Knight's move

Solutions and Notes

1	48	31	50	33	16	63	18
30	51	46	3	62	19	14	35
47	2	49	32	15	34	17	64
52	29	4	45	20	61	36	13
5	44	25	56	9	40	21	60
28	53	8	41	24	57	12	37
43	6	55	26	39	10	59	22
54	27	42	7	58	23	38	11

Knight's Tour

(visiting each square in numerical order)

(Pupils could be given a completed 'tour' with some numbers missing. The task would be to fill in the missing moves.)

29. Fraction families

Use a calculator to change $^1/_9$ to a decimal fraction. Write down exactly what you see in the display.

Now change $^2/_9$ then $^3/_9$, $^4/_9$ etc. to decimal fractions and keep a record of what appears in the display each time. Explain what you find out.

Investigate the family of elevenths. When you have worked out up to $^5/_{11}$ predict what the others are going to be and then check.

Try the family of sevenths - change $^1/_7$, $^2/_7$, $^3/_7$ etc. to decimal fractions and look for any patterns in the digits you see in the calculator display each time. Explain what you find out.

29. Fraction families

Challenges for pupils

- Use what you have learned to investigate other fraction families. Try families that start with:

$1/6$, $1/18$ etc. which are 'related' to ninths and their decimal forms are similar in some ways to the decimal forms of ninths.

$1/14$, $1/21$ etc. which are related to sevenths.

$1/22$, $1/33$ etc. which are related to elevenths.

$1/99$ which is related to both ninths and elevenths.
(The patterns generated and their connections with other fraction families are self evident so these are not listed here.)

- You might be able to find patterns in the family of thirteenths but this is a little bit more difficult.

29. Fraction families

Solutions and notes

The family of ninths gives:
    0.1111111
    0.2222222
    0.3333333
    0.4444444
    etc.

The family of elevenths gives:
    0.090909
    0.181818
    0.272727
    0.363636
    0.454545

Pupils should be able to predict at this point what the rest of the family of elevenths will be.

The family of sevenths gives:
    0.1428571
    0.2857142
    0.4285714
    0.5714285
    0.7142857
    0.8571428

Pupils should be able to recognise that:

· Each answer is composed of the same chain of digits (after the decimal point) but starting at a different point;

· The first and last digits are the same. (This is because, if the calculator could go on displaying more digits in each answer the chain of digits (142857) would repeat over and over again from the various starting points.)

29. Fraction families

Solutions and notes (continued)

The family of thirteenths gives:
    0.076923
    0.1538461
    0.2307692
    0.3076923
    0.3846153
    0.4615384
    0.5384615
    0.6153846
    0.6923076
    0.7692307
    0.8461538
    0.9230769

Pupils should be able to recognise that:

*   With the exception of $1/13$, all the numbers (after the decimal point) start and end with the same digit;
*   Some numbers use the same chain of digits:
    $2/13$, $5/13$, $6/13$, $7/13$, $8/13$ and $11/13$ all use the same chain of 153846.
    All the others use the chain 769230.

Some pupils might be able to recognise that:

*   Of the ones using 153846, there are pairs totalling one whole:
    $2/13$ and $11/13$ $5/13$ and $8/13$, $6/13$ and $7/13$
*   Of the ones using 769230 there are pairs totalling one whole:
    $1/13$ and $12/13$, $3/13$ and $10/13$, $4/13$ and $9/13$

30. Colourways

You will need:

•   a 5 x 5 board like the one below;
•   25 counters, five each of five different colours.

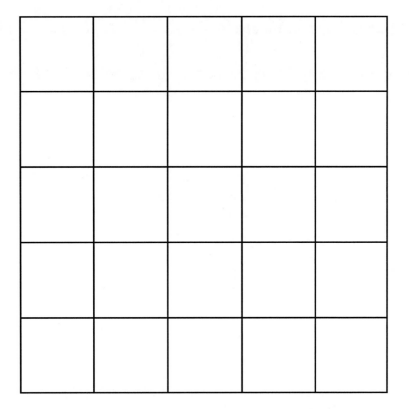

Using the five counters of one colour, place them on the board so that no two are in a horizontal, vertical or diagonal line with each other.

Do the same with each of the five colours until all the counters are placed.

Remember, no two counters of the same colour must be in a line with each other.

Hint: If you have done the 'Knight's Move' investigation you might find it helpful here.

30. Colourways

Challenges for pupils

- Try other boards of different sizes. Can it be done, for example, on a 3 x 3 board, a 7 x 7 board etc.?

- Try 'even' boards, for example, 4 x 4, 6 x 6 etc. Can it still be done?

- Explain why you think it can/cannot be done on any 'odd' board and any 'even' board.

30. Colourways

Solutions

This is one way of completing the task on a 5 x 5 board:

R	G	B	W	Y
W	Y	R	G	B
G	B	W	Y	R
Y	R	G	B	W
B	W	Y	R	G

Using: R - Red,
G - Green, B - Blue,
Y - Yellow, W - White

A 3 x 3 baord cannot be completed according to the rules. There are three possible start positions for the first counter placed (plus all their reflections and rotations):

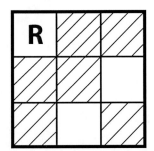 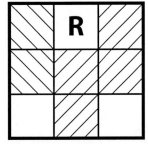 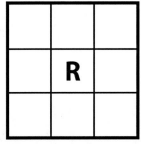

The first two leave only two possible positions for the other counters of the same colour and these are in line with each other. The third eliminates all other positions for the second and third counters.

This is one way of completing the task on a 7 x 7 board:

R	G	B	Y	W	P	Pu
P	Pu	R	G	B	Y	W
Y	W	P	Pu	R	G	B
G	B	Y	W	P	Pu	R
Pu	R	G	B	Y	W	P
W	P	Pu	R	G	B	Y
B	Y	W	P	Pu	R	G

Using: R - Red,
G - Green, B - Blue,
Y - Yellow, W - White
P - Pink, Pu - Purple

31. Is it magic?

Choose any two **different** digits from 1 to 9.

Use these digits to make four different two digit numbers.

Add your four numbers together.

Divide this total by the sum of the two digits you started with.

This is an example:

Digits chosen are 3 and 4 and their sum is 7
The four numbers that can be made using these digits are 34, 43, 33 & 44
Their total is 154
154 ÷ 7 = 22

Try other sets of two digits.

What happens?

Will this happen with all possible pairs of digits? You could try them all - there are 36 possible pairs - 1 and 2, 1 and 3, 1 and 4 etc., 2 and 3, 2 and 4, 2 and 5 and so on.

Or you could try to explain why it will always happen, or why there are some exceptions.

31. Is it magic?

Challenges for pupils

- Investigate using three different digits from which to make two digit numbers, for example:
Using 2, 3 and 4 you can make 23, 32, 22, 33, 24, 42, 44, 34 and 43
What would you divide their total by? *(2 + 3 + 4)* Will the answer still be 22 in all cases? *(The answer will always be 33.)*

- What if you use 4, 5, 6, ... 9 different digits to make two digit numbers? *(When n is the number of different digits used the answer will always be 11n.)*

- Investigate what happens when you use two different digits to make all the possible three digit numbers. (Example: using 2 and 3 you can make 223, 322, 233, 332, 232, 323, 222 and 333.) *(Their total divided by the sum of the digits will be 444 because each digit appears four times as a hundred, four times as a ten and four times as a unit.)*

- How many three digit numbers can you make from 3, 4, 5, ... 9 different digits. Warning! There are a lot of three digit numbers you can make from all 9 digits! Can you predict what the answers would be if you totalled them all and divided them by the sum of the nine digits?

31. Is it magic?

Solutions and notes

All possible pairs of digits operated upon in this way will result in the answer 22.

Pupils could show this by testing every possible combination of two digits (not unreasonable given that there are 36 combinations and it could be done collaboratively).

The general proof lies in the fact that in any pair of digits (3 and 4) operated upon in this way, each digit will appear twice as a ten (34 and 33, 43 and 44) and twice as a unit (43 and 33, 34 and 44). This can be viewed as:

Sum of the numbers 34, 43, 33 and 44 or

2 x (3 + 4) tens and 2 x (3 + 4) units

When 2 x (3 + 4) tens (or units) are divided by (3 + 4) the result is 2 tens (or units)

There are 64 three digit numbers that can be made using 4 different digits, 125 with 5 digits, 216 with 6, 343 with 7, 512 using 8 and 729 using all 9.

32. In a spin

You need one copy of each of the spinners on page 130

An easy way to use them is with a paper clip and pencil:

Put the point of the pencil through one end of the paper clip.
With the paper clip in position on the pencil, place the pencil point on the centre of the spinner.
Flick the paper clip so that it spins round the pencil point.
Read the number that it stops on.

If you were to spin the paper clip 100 times on each spinner, can you predict which one would produce more 4s?

How will you check this? What is the simplest way to record your results? Ask someone to help you do all the spins.

Was your prediction correct?

Change the numbers on the spinners. Put the numbers 4, 2, 5, 3, 3 and 3 on the hexagonal one and 4, 5, 2, 2, 3, 3, 3 and 3 on the octagonal one.

If you were to spin the paper clip 100 times on each spinner, which one would produce more 3s? Explain how you know you are right, without having to do 200 spins.

Which one would produce more 4s? Explain how you know you are right.

32. In a spin

Challenges for pupils

- Use copies of the blank spinners on page 131 to produce:

  - Two which will give a 1 in 4 chance of producing an even number
  - One which will give a 2 in 5 chance of producing an odd number
  - Two which will give a 1 in 3 chance of producing a prime number
  - One which will give a 1 in 5 chance of producing a square number
  - Number all of them so that they each give a better than 1 in 2 chance of producing a multiple of 5

- Make up some challenges of your own about spinners. You might even like to design a different spinner.

32. In a spin

Solutions and notes

Using the original spinners, both would produce the same number of 4s. Each spinner has the number 4 in half of its sections and so has a 1 in 2 chance of producing a 4.

Pupils should be encouraged to think carefully about how to record the spins in the easiest, simplest way (perhaps a tally chart).

The amended spinners have a 1 in 2 chance of producing a 3. The hexagonal spinner will produce more 4s. Although both spinners have only one 4, the hexagonal one has only 6 numbers in total (therefore gives a 1 in 6 chance of a 4) whereas the octagonal one has 8 numbers in total (therefore gives a 1 in 8 chance of a 4).

32. In a spin

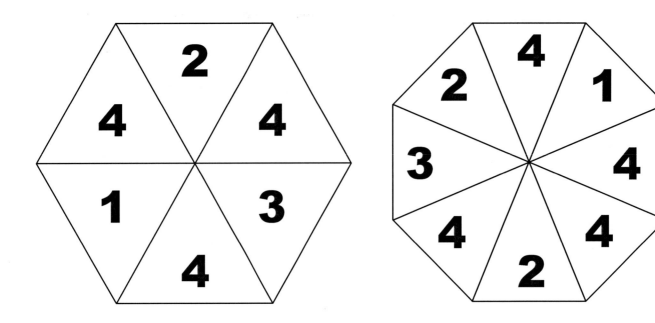

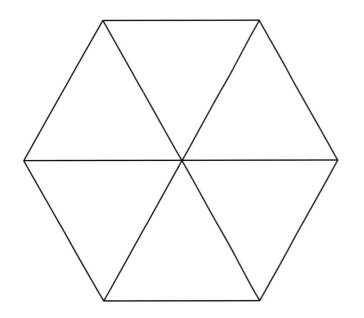

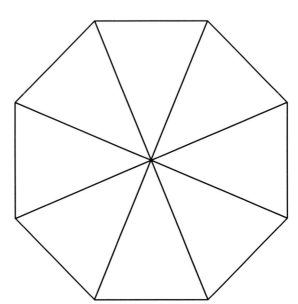

32. In a spin

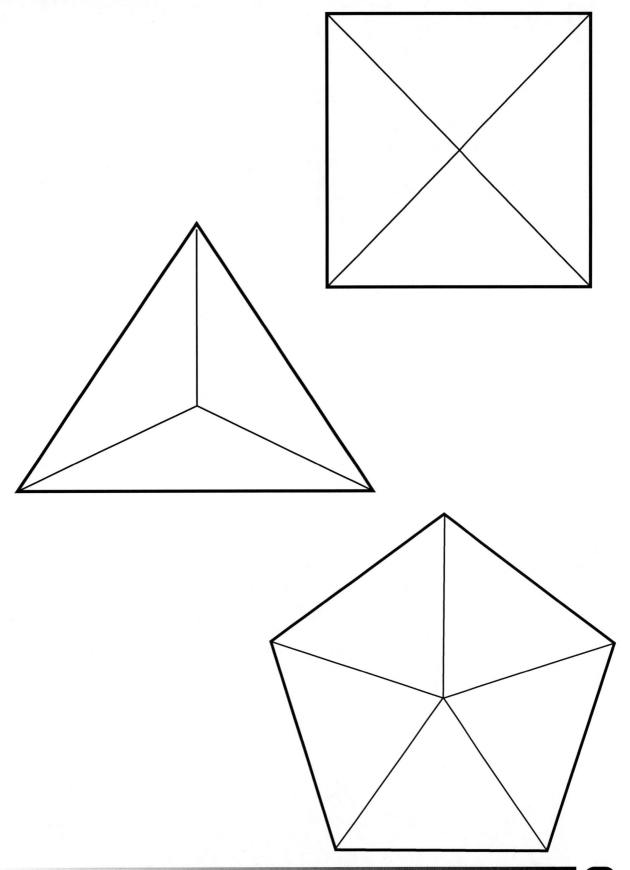

33. Shapes and middles

Draw a large triangle using a pencil and ruler. (Your drawing must be careful and accurate.)

Measure each side as accurately as you can and mark its middle point.

Join these middle points carefully, using a ruler, to make another triangle.

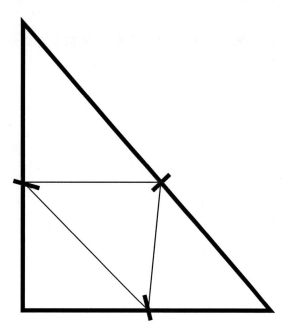

Measure the sides and angles of the larger triangle, and the sides an angles of the smaller triangle. What do you notice?

Use a copy of the triangles on page 136 to find out whether this happens with all triangles.

Compare the area of the larger and the smaller triangle. (You can do this by cutting out.) What can you say about their areas? Cut your large triangle into the four smaller ones. What can you say about the smaller ones?

33. Shapes and middles

Challenges for pupils

- Investigate quadrilaterals in the same way. There are some to start you off on page 137. When you have tried these, draw some more quadrilaterals of your own. You could try a trapezium, a kite, and some irregular quadrilaterals.

  - Look at the smaller shapes that are produced in the middle of your starting shape.
  - Can you name the shapes?
  - How does the area of the large shape compare to the area of the small one.

- What do you think you would find if you worked on a pentagon, a hexagon, an octagon etc. Find some shapes to draw around if you can't draw your own shapes, but remember, they don't have to be regular shapes.

33. Shapes and middles

Solutions and notes

The sides of the smaller triangle are each half the length of the parallel side in the large triangle. Angles in the small triangle are the same as the angles in the large triangle. Pupils should be familiar with the fact that we call these **similar** triangles - exactly the same shape but different sizes.

The smaller triangle is one quarter the area of the larger one.

The four smaller triangles are congruent - identical in shape and size.

Quadrilaterals produce 'middle' shapes different from the starting shape but with half the area (this can be demonstrated by cutting or folding).

33. Shapes and middles

33. Shapes and middles

34. The Chinese puzzle

Another name for the Chinese puzzle is a tangram.

A tangram is made from seven pieces cut fom a single square.

You will find a tangram to copy, cut up and work with on page 142.

One of the tangram pieces is a square (much smaller than the one from which the pieces are made of course).

Is it possible to make a square using two of the tangram pieces? Three of them? Four, five, six of them?

Use squared paper to help you to record your findings.

34. The Chinese puzzle

Challenges for pupils

•   It is possible to make slightly larger squares with a hole, using the seven pieces. For example, you can make a square with a missing papallelogram, a missing square and a missing triangle:

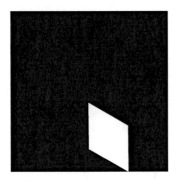 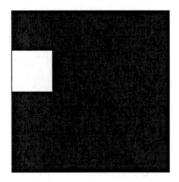 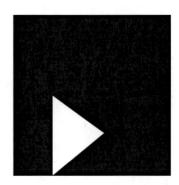

Can you find any more?

•   It is also possible to make squares with two triangles missing. These are some examples of at least 60 different ones! How many can you find?

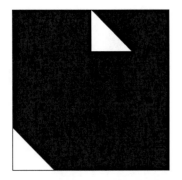  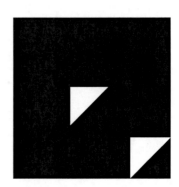

•   You might like to find out the history of the Chinese puzzle.

34. The Chinese puzzle

Some solutions

These are some suggestions for making squares with various numbers of pieces:

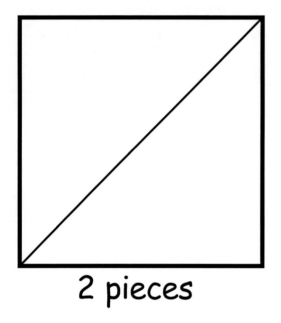

2 pieces

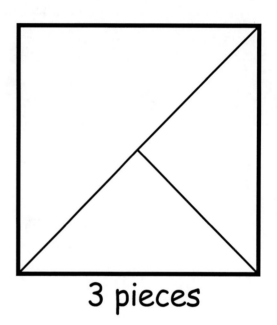

3 pieces

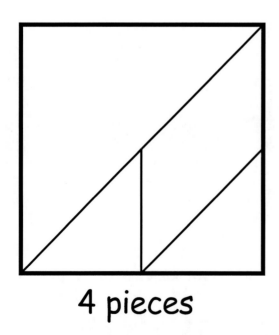

4 pieces

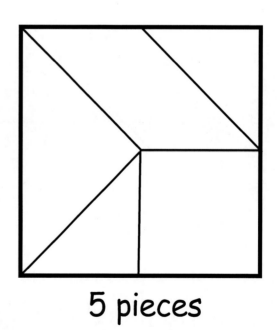

5 pieces

Pupils will probably find others as they work.

34. The Chinese puzzle

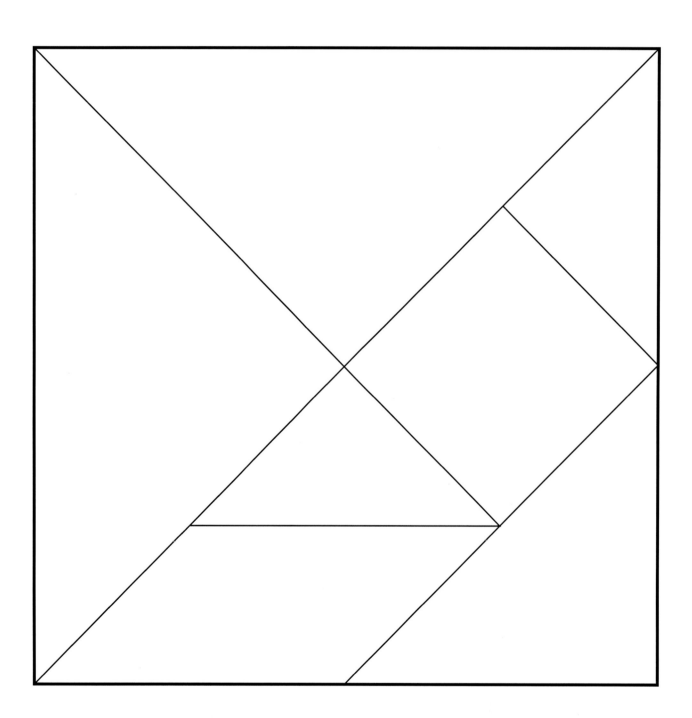

35. Regions and maps

Find some A5 and A4 sheets of paper. On an A5 sheet draw a few ruler lines from one side of the paper to the opposite side, like this:

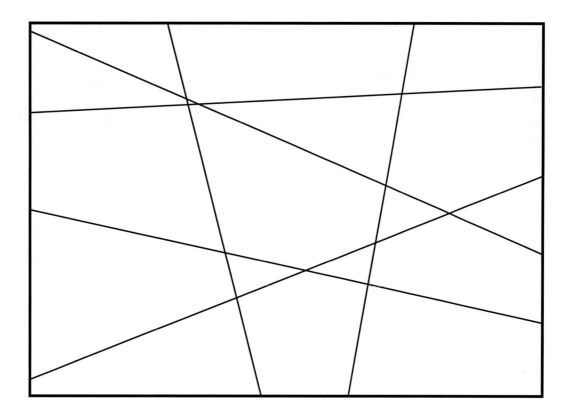

What is the minimum number of colours you need to colour the whole sheet if no two touching regions can be the same colour (regions touching **only** corner to corner can be the same colour).

Don't draw too many lines to start with.

Do the same thing again on another sheet of paper, but this time draw a few more lines. Do you need more colours? If you do, is it because there are more lines or more regions or both? If you don't need more colours, why not?

Repeat a few times, each time on another sheet of paper with even more lines.

If you find A5 paper too small as you draw more lines, then use A4.

What have you found out?

35. Regions and maps

Challenges for pupils

- Use a map of the British Isles with the county boundaries marked on it. What is the maximum number of colours you would need to colour it in so that no two touching counties are the same colour?

- Try this with the maps of other countries - the USA, Canada and Australia are good ones to use.

- Two men called Kenneth Appel and Wolfgang Haken did a lot of work about colouring maps. You might like to find out about them.

35. Regions and Maps

Some solutions

Outcomes will be different depending on the arrangement of lines and regions, but the maximum number of colours needed for any arrangement is 4.

This can be demonstrated using the following diagrams:

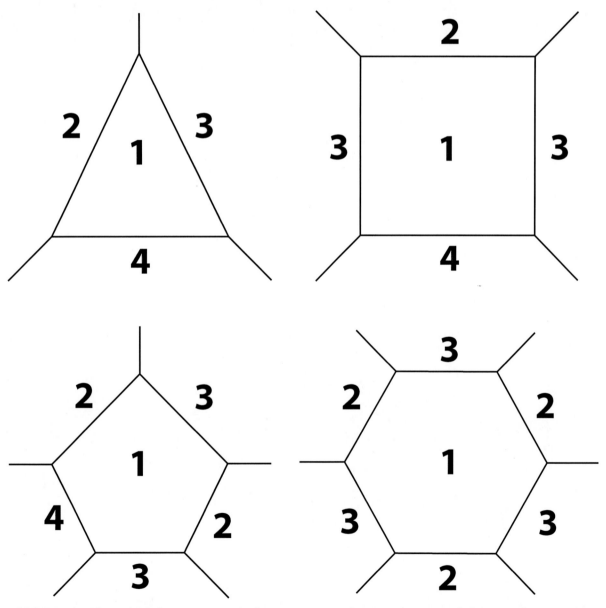

In 1976 Appel and Haken proved that you need a maximum of four colours on a map so that the colour of any two regions next to each other are different. Some maps can be coloured using fewer than four colours.